Books in the series

To Bee or Not To Bee
The Fast and the Curious
Leave a Light on for Me

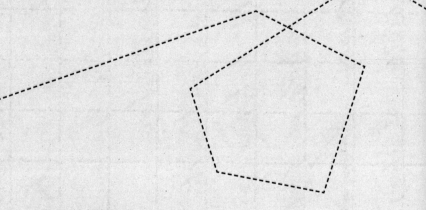

First published 2021 by Honey Craft

ISBN 978-1-8384778-1-3

Text copyright © Jayne Williams, Illustration © Keith Turner
Typeset and design by Mooli

A CIP catalogue record for this book is available from the British Library

Printed in Leicester, UK by SBS Print Group on 100% recycled paper
100% carbon balanced Certificate number CBP008769
www.carbonbalancedpaper.com

WORLD
LAND
TRUST™
www.carbonbalancedpaper.com
CBP007580

www.honeycraft.org

THE FAST AND THE CURIOUS

Jayne Williams

Illustrated by Keith Turner

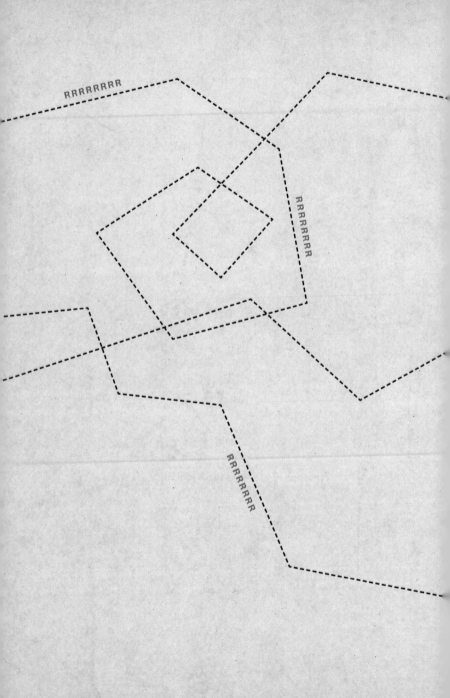

G-Nat is in a full panic

'Can't find! Can't find!
Can't find! RRRRRRRR'

Having lost a prized possession
The best DJ decks in Leicester
Which happen to be made
From two round specs of dust

They must be found
Everyone's out looking
But they could be gone
Forever?

'What am I gonna do?
Can't let my Fam down
My Crowd
My Crew
My G's'

There'll be major disappointment
Among that cloud of gnats
Who are well up for
Having a dance
Bustin' some shapes
Making some moves
Later at the Library

G-Nat loves a rave

'I love raving, I do'

G-Nat also loves reading

'I love reading, I do'

Music in Libraries
Brings G-Nat's two favourite
Things together

Performing on a stage
Made from a chunky novel
With hundreds of pages
Is such a thrill

G-Nat will be tonight's headline act
At the mini beast mobile disco
Which takes place every month
At midnight
In a different Library
Each time

Mini beasts of all kinds
Gather
For a fun night out

Pork Pie Library proudly presents

MIDNIGHT FESTIVAL

HEADLINE ACT

G-NAT
ROX THE DECKS

Snake Bugg

BEE T S

WEEVIL ROCK U

AKBee48 HEADLICE

SPY-DERS B-HIVES HUM DINGER

STING | BEETLES | XL ANT | LUNA TICK | BED BUGS

VANILLA LICE | COOLANT | THE WANNA BEES | ABee ⚡CD | FRISBEE

G-Nat is a super fly DJ
A pest on the decks
Scratching those records
And itching them too

G-Nat is a multi-talented
Multi-disciplinary artist
A mini beast
With a specialism in beats
And graffiti

Those DJ decks must be found
Those tiny round specs of dust
Must be somewhere

'When somet is lost
Go back to where you
last had it
I heard a hooman say that

Where were it last?'

G-Nat flits between Libraries
From Central
To Beaumont Leys
Braunstone
And
Pork Pie Library

G-Nat only has two tiny wings
But can move super-fast
And flits around the libraries
At turbo gnat speed

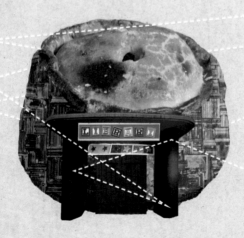

But G-Nat is also incredibly
Curious

'Decks? Decks? Decks?
OOO look
A book about Bees

Decks? Decks? Decks?
Are books made of trees?

Decks? Decks? Decks?
My neez are a bit nobberly?

Got to find them decks
Where could they be?'

As you can see
G-Nat can lose focus
On the task
In hand
Quite easily

G-Nat is bursting with energy
And is a lean, mean curiosity machine

Having been hatched on page 56
Of a book about Spaceships
On the third shelf
Of the Sci-Fi section

Libraries have always been
G-Nat's favourite places to be
With books having a massive effect
On this miniscule insect

At first
G-Nat was afraid of words
With letters being
Twice the size
G-Nat would cry
And take comfort in a full stop

Growth kicks in
G-Nat begins to read
Those letters aren't so scary
Anymore

Letters turn into words
Words into sentences
Sentences into paragraphs
Before too long
G-Nat has fallen in love
With a semicolon

'Wots going on?'

A bit of back story for the reader

'You tryin to embarrass me?'

Just spelling out your
Admiration for punctuation

'I wasn't born yesterday'

Indeed
G-Nat was born last week
And is rapidly becoming
A love-struck teenager

'Concentrate!
Help me find me decks'

Best ask a Librarian

Have U seen me decks?'

Have U seen me decks?

'Don't be scared
Am no threat

Peepul think us gnats are evil
Coz we SUCK BLOOD
But am vegan thru n thru
So, you don't have to worry
Bout me biting U'

Nobody seems to have a clue
What G-Nat is on about

G-Nat is tiny
The size of a sesame seed
Or a full stop
Or a small blob of snot from a sneeze
This Library team
Are patient beings
But may struggle to see
G-Nat's teeny weeny decks
Made from two round specs of dust
Especially in a Library
Full of old books

Hang on
There's a big announcement
On Insectagram

 # Insectagram

'If G-Nat fails to locate those decks
We'll have no choice but to make
Headlice the new headline act'

Headlice are the band from up north
They're not particularly the best
But they play all their own instruments
Which puts them head and shoulders
Above the rest

'Decks? Decks? Decks?'

G-Nat is in a right flap
With the need to find the decks
Being cranked up

Have those two tiny specs of dust
Gotten lost
Between the pages
Of a picture book?

Or left
On a Librarian's desk
Hidden under a coffee cup?

Flinged
Out of an open window
On a gust of wind?

Or swept up
With a dustpan and brush?

Where could they be?

'Got to find them decks.
Don't want to let everyone down.
OOO, look, some sweeteez
Don't mind if I do'

It's easy to be distracted
By a sugary treat

G-Nat has a policy
Of living life to the fullest
Even on the dullest of days

No wasting time being miserable
We're not on this planet for long
In fact, a gnat
Might only live for one
Month

You never know when you might
Be flattened under a flip flop
Go splat on a car windscreen
Get eaten by a duck
Squished between the pages
Of a hard back book

SPLAT

These are the reasons why
G-Nat won't let
Those missing decks
Ruin the whole night

So, G-Nat lives life to the max
And will be tonight's headline act
With or without
Those tiny specs
Of tuneful dust

There's no need to fret
Or get upset

Just trust the
immense talent
That lies within
That brain and body
The size of a pin head
Or a few grains of salt

It's not G-Nat's fault
Those decks have gone missing
And anyway

However miniscule you may be
If you have the bravery
To show the world
What you're made of
You can become

TWO FEET TALL!

tiny
+
bravery
= huge

All you need
Is a chunk of confidence
And a slice of self esteem
To be anything you want to be

Yes, it's great to have decks
But it is you
That brings the beats
And creates the tunes

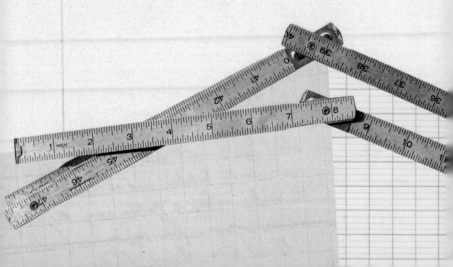

G-Nat takes to the Novella stage
Mini beasts gather
They're well up for a rave

Flies to the mic
Goes rogue
Freestyle
Spits some ripping lyrics
Proper winging it

The crowd goes wild
(They are mini beasts after all)
Even Headlice clap their claws
The round of applause is raucous

Ants swarm the dance floor
Beetles flick their
Mop top hair
Bees spray paint
Messages of positivity
Every insect is buzzing

'Dance like nobody is listenin
Sing like nobody is lookin
Don't let anythin
Hold U back'

And with that
G-Nat
Drops the mic

DID YOU KNOW?
FACTS ABOUT GNATS

* Fungus gnat adults live for one to two weeks and complete one life cycle in about 18-30 days

* Female Gnats can lay up to 300 eggs a day

* Gnats go through four life stages – egg, larvae, pupae and adult

* Potentially Dangerous!? Not to people, but possibly to household plants and seedlings

* They can be both biting and non-biting. The biting ones are often called midges

* Gnats feed themselves and live on rotten fruit and vegetable's

* Male Gnats don't bite and primarily live on nectar and flower juices